ELVIS' FORTY GREATEST

KU-600-639

EXCLUSIVE DISTRIBUTORS
MUSIC SALES LIMITED
78 NEWMAN STREET
LONDON W1P 3LA

WISE PUBLICATIONS
LONDON/NEW YORK/SYDNEY

MY BABY LEFT ME

WORDS & MUSIC BY
ARTHUR CRUDUP

Moderately Bright

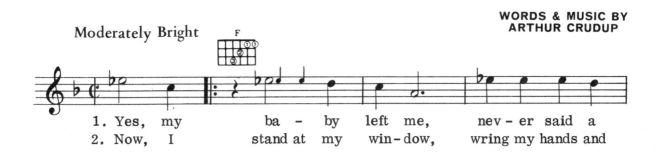

1. Yes, my ba - by left me, nev - er said a
2. Now, I stand at my win - dow, wring my hands and

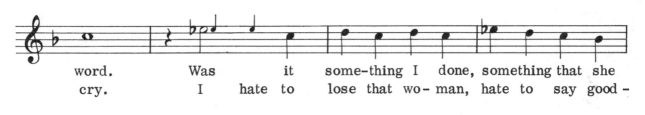

word. Was it some-thing I done, something that she
cry. I hate to lose that wo - man, hate to say good -

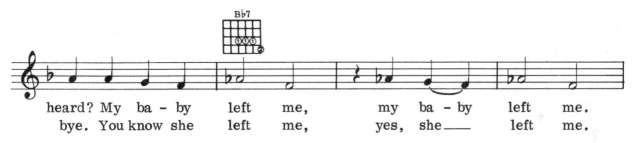

heard? My ba - by left me, my ba - by left me.
bye. You know she left me, yes, she___ left me.

My ba - by e - ven left me,___ nev - er said a

word._____ 2. Now, I

Copyright © 1956 by Elvis Presley Music Inc., New York, USA.
Carlin Music Corp., 14 New Burlington Street, London, W1X 1AE for the United Kingdom of Great Britain and Northern
Ireland, South Africa, Eire, Israel, and the British Dominions, Colonies, Overseas Territories and Dependencies
(excluding Canada, Australia and New Zealand) and Greece.

BLUE SUEDE SHUES

WORDS & MUSIC BY
CARL LEE PERKINS

Bright tempo (not too fast)

CHORUS

Well it's one for the mon-ey two for the show,

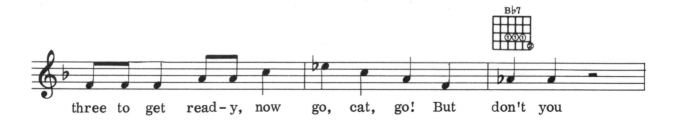

three to get read-y, now go, cat, go! But don't you

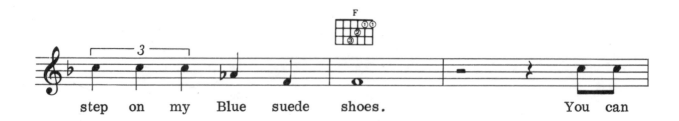

step on my Blue suede shoes. You can

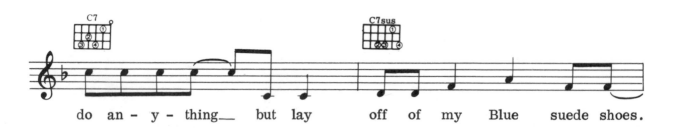

do an-y-thing__ but lay off of my Blue suede shoes.

Well, you can knock me down,
Burn my house,

Copyright © MCMLVI by Hi Lo Music.
Rights assigned to Hill and Range Songs Inc., New York, USA.
Carlin Music Corp., 14 New Burlington Street, London, W1X 1AE.
for the British Empire (excluding Canada, Australasia and South Africa) and the Republic of Ireland.

LOVE ME TENDER

WORDS & MUSIC BY
ELVIS PRESLEY & VERA MATSON

VERSE

1. Love me ten - der, love me sweet; Nev - er let me
2. Love me ten - der, love me long; Take me to your
3. Love me ten - der, love me dear; Tell me you are
4. When at last my dreams come true, Dar - ling, this I

go.   You have made my life com - plete,
heart.   For it's there that I be - long,
mine.   I'll be yours through all the years,
know.   Hap - pi - ness will fol - low you

CHORUS

And I love you so.
And we'll nev - er part.   Love me ten - der, love me true,
Till the end of time.
Ev - 'ry - where you go

All my dreams ful - fill.   For, my dar - lin', I love you,

1
And I al - ways will.

2
And I al - ways will.

Copyright © 1956 by Elvis Presley Music Inc., New York, USA.
Carlin Music Corp., 14 New Burlington Street, London, W1X 1AE
for the British Empire (excluding Canada, Australasia, New Zealand and South Africa) and the Republic of Ireland.

All Shook Up

Medium Shuffle Rhythm

WORDS & MUSIC BY
OTIS BLACKWELL & ELVIS PRESLEY

Copyright © 1957 by Shalimar Music Corp., New York.
Sole selling and licensing agent for the British Isles and British Empire
(excluding Canada, Australasia) and Republic of Ireland.
Carlin Music Corp., 14 New Burlington Street, London, W1X 1AE.

have such luck? I'm in love! I'm All shook up!_ Mm

mm, oh, oh, yeah, yeah!_____

1. Please don't ask what's on my mind, I'm a
2. Tongue gets tied when I try to speak, My___

lit - tle mixed up but I'm feel - in' fine___ When I'm
in - side shakes like a leaf on a tree, There's

near___ that girl that___ I___ love best, My___
on - ly one cure for this soul of mine, That's to

heart beats so it___ scares me to death! She
have the girl that I love so fine!

GOT A LOTTA LIVIN' TO DO

WORDS & MUSIC BY
AARON SCHROEDER & BEN WEISMAN

Bright tempo

VERSE

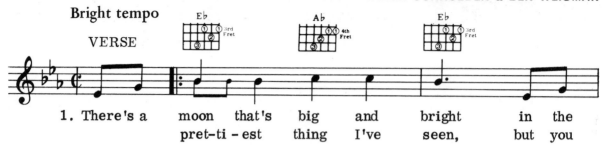

1. There's a moon that's big and bright in the
pret-ti-est thing I've seen, but you

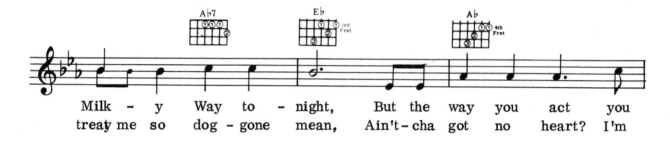

Milk - y Way to - night, But the way you act you
treat me so dog - gone mean, Ain't-cha got no heart? I'm

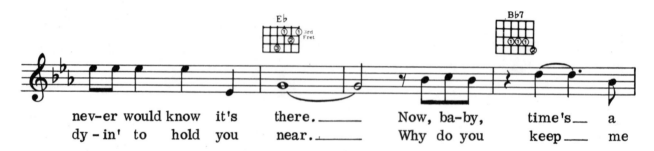

nev-er would know it's there._____ Now, ba-by, time's__ a
dy-in' to hold you near._____ Why do you keep___ me

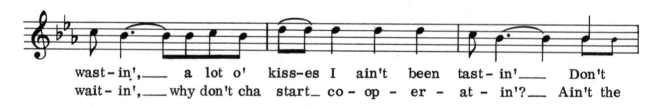

wast-in',___ a lot o' kiss-es I ain't been tast-in'___ Don't
wait-in',___ why don't cha start__ co - op - er - at - in'?___ Ain't the

know a - bout you but I'm a gon - na get my share._____
things__ I say the things__ you__ wan - na hear?_____

Copyright © 1957 by Gladys Music Inc., New York, USA.
Carlin Music Corp., 14 New Burlington Street, London, W1X 1AE for the territory of the United Kingdom of
Great Britain and Northern Ireland, Eire, Israel, and the British Dominions, Colonies, Overseas Territories and
Dependencies (excluding Canada, Australia and New Zealand).
The use of this song with any other music is expressly prohibited

CHORUS

Oh, yes, I've — Got — a lot o' liv-in' to do, —

Whole lot o' lov-in' to do. — *Spoken* Come on ba-by! To

make it fun it takes two. ——— Oh, yes, I've — got — a lot o'

liv-in' to do, — Whole lot o' lov-in' to do, — And there's

no one who I'd rath-er do it with - a than

1 you! ——— 2. You're the **2** you! ———

[LET ME BE YOUR]
TEDDY BEAR

Medium bright Rock

WORDS & MUSIC BY
KAL MANN & BERNIE LOWE

1. Ba - by let me be your lov - in' Ted - dy
2. Ba - by let me be a - round you ev - 'ry

Bear. Put a chain a - round my neck___ and
night. Run your fin - gers through my hair___ and

lead me an - y - where. Oh let me be___ your Ted-dy
cud - dle me real tight.

Bear.___ I don't want to be your ti - ger 'cause

ti - gers play too rough. I don't want to be your

Copyright © 1957 by Gladys Music Inc., New York, USA.
Carlin Music Corp., 14 New Burlington Street, London, W1X 1AE for the territory of United Kingdom of Great Britain
and Northern Ireland, Eire, Israel, and the British Dominions, Colonies, Overseas Territories and Dependencies
(excluding Canada, Australia and New Zealand).
The use of this song with any other music is expressly prohibited.

li - on 'cause li - ons ain't the kind you love e -

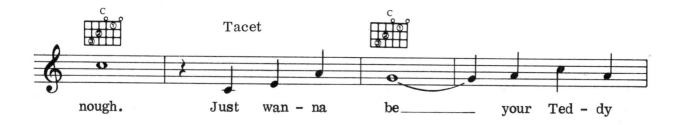

nough. Just wan - na be_____ your Ted - dy

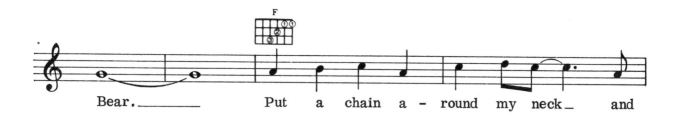

Bear._____ Put a chain a - round my neck_ and

lead me an - y - where. Oh let me be_____ your Ted - dy

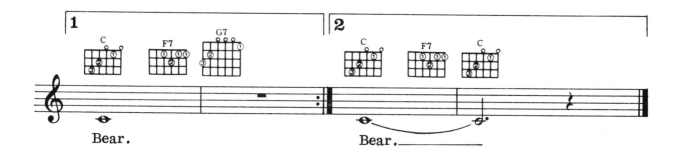

1 Bear. **2** Bear._____

OLD SHEP

WORDS & MUSIC BY
CLYDE (RED) FOLEY

© Copyright 1940 by M. M. Cole Publishing Co., Chicago.
For the British Commonwealth (excepting Canada and Australasia) the property of
Lawrence Wright Music Co. Ltd., 24 Bruton Street, London, W1X 7AH.

DON'T

WORDS & MUSIC BY
JERRY LEIBER & MIKE STOLLER

Slowly

CHORUS

Don't, don't, that's what you say Each
Don't, don't, leave my em - brace, For

time that I hold you ___ this way. ___ When I feel like
here in my arms is ___ your place. ___ When the night grows

this and I want to kiss you, ba - by, don't say
cold and I want to hold you, ba - by, don't say

1 don't. ___

2 don't. ___

If you think that this is just a game I'm

Copyright © 1957 by Elvis Presley Music Inc., New York, NY
Carlin Music Corp., 14 New Burlington Street, London, W1X 1AE for the British Isles and the British Empire
(excluding Canada, South Africa, Australia and New Zealand) and the Republic of Ireland.

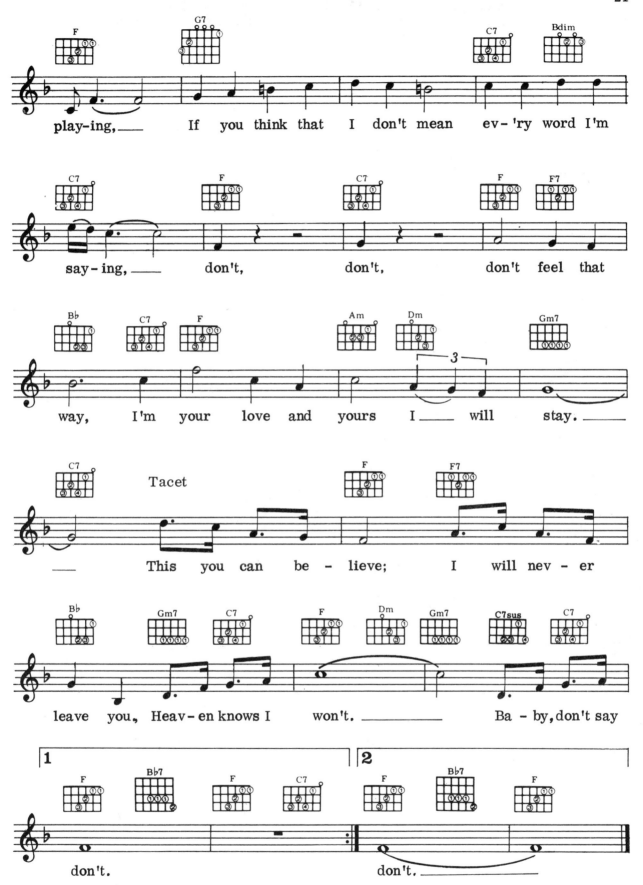

Hard Headed Woman

WORDS & MUSIC BY
CLAUDE DE METRUIS

Bright Rock
CHORUS

Well a Hard head-ed wo-man, a soft hearted man
Now A-dam told Eve:__ Lis-ten here to me;

Been the cause of trou-ble ev-er since the world be-gan. Oh,
Don't you let me catch you mess-in' 'round that ap-ple tree.

yeah, Ev-er since the world be-gan.__ Uh-huh-huh.

A hard head-ed woman been a thorn in the side of

1 man.   2. Now

2 man.

Copyright © 1958 by Gladys Music Inc., New York, USA.
Carlin Music Corp., 14 New Burlington Street, London, W1X 1AE for the British Isles, British Empire
(excluding Canada, South Africa, Australia and New Zealand) and the Republic of Ireland.

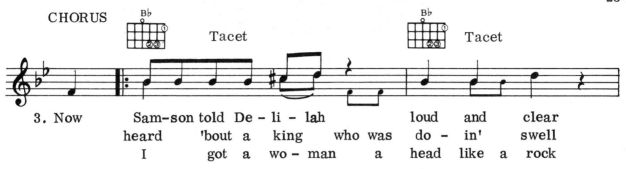

CHORUS

3. Now Sam-son told De - li - lah loud and clear
heard 'bout a king who was do - in' swell
I got a wo - man a head like a rock

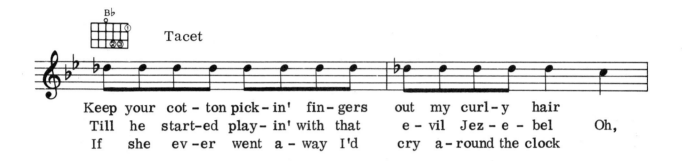

Keep your cot - ton pick - in' fin - gers out my curl - y hair
Till he start - ed play - in' with that e - vil Jez - e - bel Oh,
If she ev - er went a - way I'd cry a - round the clock

yeah, Ev - er since the world be - gan.___ Uh - huh - huh,___

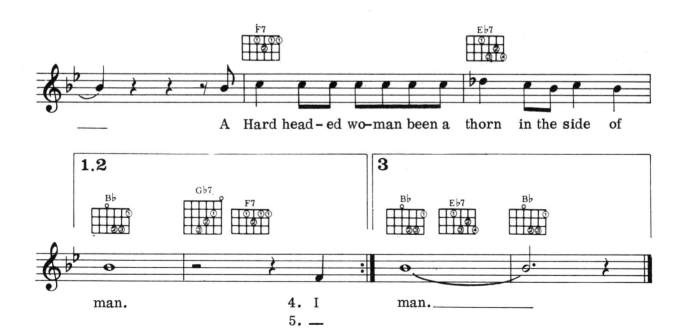

___ A Hard head - ed wo - man been a thorn in the side of

1.2   3

man.   4. I   man.___
        5. ___

King Creole

WORDS & MUSIC BY
JERRY LEIBER & MIKE STOLLER

Bright Rock

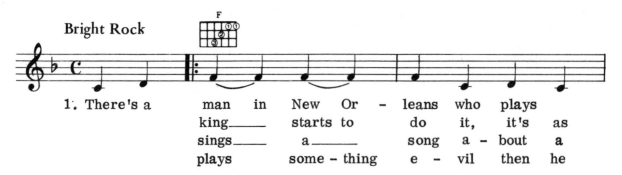

1. There's a man in New Or - leans who plays
king___ starts to do it, it's as
sings___ a___ song a - bout a
plays some - thing e - vil then he

rock and roll.___ He's a gui - tar___ man___
good as done.___ He___ holds___ his gui -
craw - dad hole.___ He___ sings___ a___
plays some-thing sweet.___ No___ mat - ter what he

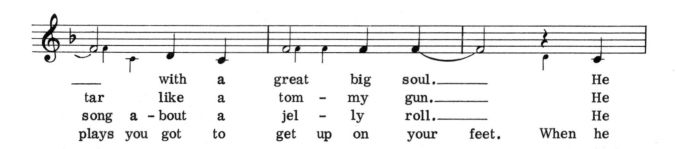

___ with a great big soul.___ He
tar like a tom - my gun.___ He
song a - bout a jel - ly roll.___ He
plays you got to get up on your feet. When he

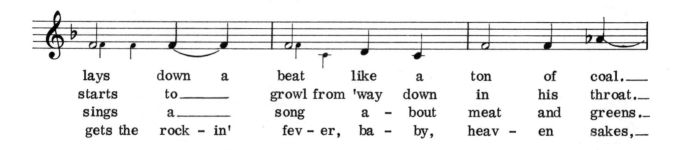

lays down a beat like a ton of coal.___
starts to___ growl from 'way down in his throat.___
sings a___ song a - bout meat and greens.___
gets the rock - in' fev - er, ba - by, heav - en sakes,___

Copyright © 1958 by Elvis Presley Music Inc., New York, NY.
Carlin Music Corp., 14 New Burlington Street, London, W1X 1AE for the British Isles and the British Empire
(excluding Canada, South Africa, Australia and New Zealand) and the Republic of Ireland.

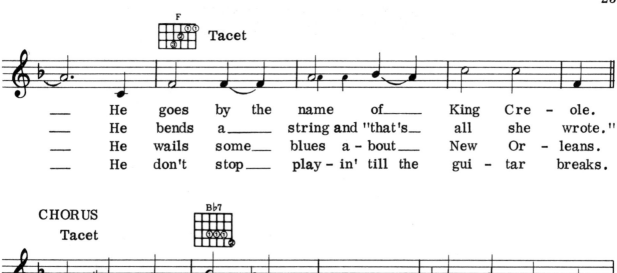

	He	goes	by	the	name	of___	King	Cre	-	ole.
	He	bends	a___	string and	"that's___	all	she	wrote."
	He	wails	some___	blues	a - bout___	New	Or	-	leans.
	He	don't	stop___	play - in' till the	gui	-	tar	breaks.

CHORUS
Tacet

You know he's gone, gone, gone, Jump - in' like a

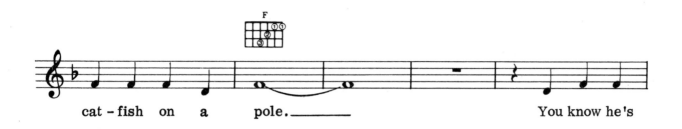

cat - fish on a pole.___ You know he's

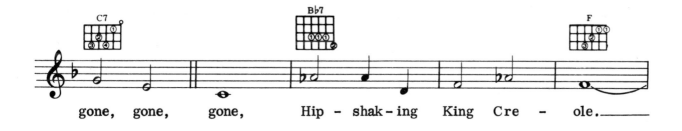

gone, gone, gone, Hip - shak - ing King Cre - ole.___

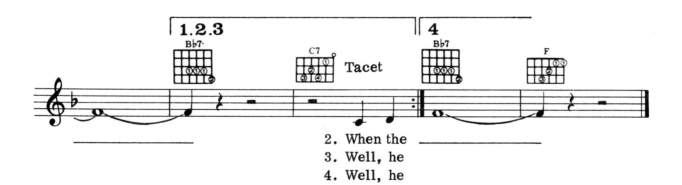

___

2. When the ___
3. Well, he
4. Well, he

Jailhouse Rock

WORDS & MUSIC BY
JERRY LEIBER & MIKE STOLLER

Medium bright Rock

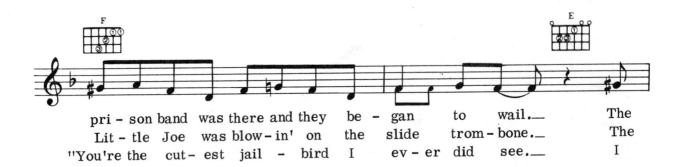

1. The war-den threw a par-ty in the coun-ty jail___ The
2. Spi-der Mur-phy play'd the ten-or sax-o-phone.___
3. Number For-ty-sev-en said to Num-ber Three.___

pri-son band was there and they be-gan to wail.___ The
Lit-tle Joe was blow-in' on the slide trom-bone.___ The
"You're the cut-est jail-bird I ev-er did see.___ I

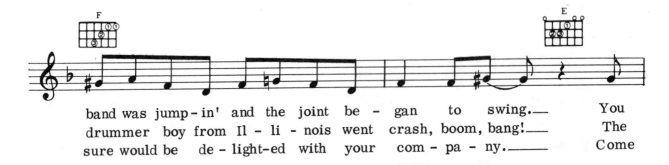

band was jump-in' and the joint be-gan to swing.___ You
drummer boy from Il-li-nois went crash, boom, bang!___ The
sure would be de-light-ed with your com-pa-ny.___ Come

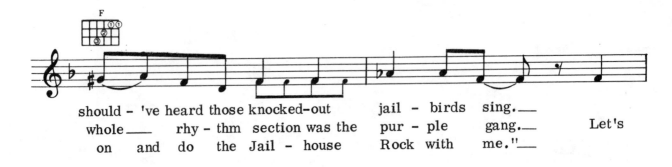

should-'ve heard those knocked-out jail-birds sing.___
whole___ rhy-thm section was the pur-ple gang.___ Let's
on and do the Jail-house Rock with me."___

Copyright © 1957 by Elvis Presley Music Inc., New York, USA.
Carlin Music Corp., 14 New Burlington Street, London, W1X 1AE for the territory of the United Kingdom of Great Britain
and Northern Ireland, Eire, Israel, and the British Dominions, Colonies, Overseas Territories and Dependencies.
The use of this song with any other music is expressly prohibited.

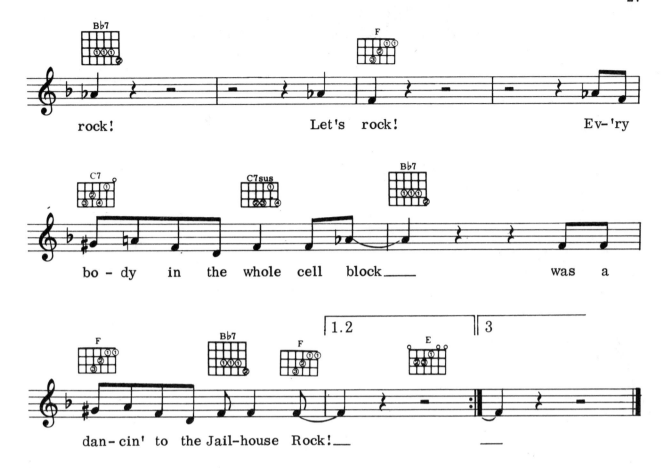

rock!   Let's   rock!   Ev-'ry

bo - dy   in   the   whole   cell   block___   was   a

dan - cin'   to   the   Jail-house   Rock!___

EXTRA CHORUSES

4.   The sad sack was a-sittin' on a block of stone,
      Way over in the corner weeping all alone.
      The warden said, "Hey buddy, don't you be no square,
      If you can't find a partner, use a wooden chair!"
      Let's rock, etc.

5.   Shifty Henry said to Bugs, "For Heaven's sake,
      No one s lookin', now's our chance to make a break."
      Bugsy turned to Shifty and he said, "Nix, nix,
      I wanna stick around a while and get my kicks,"
      Let's rock, etc.

BIG HUNK OF LOVE

Bright Rock

WORDS & MUSIC BY
AARON SCHROEDER & SID WYCHE

CHORUS

Hey, ba-by! I ain't ask-in' much of you.

No no, no no no no no no no, ba-by, I ain't ask-in' much of

you. Just a big-a big-a big-a hunk o' love will

do._____ 1. Don't be a stin-gy lit-tle ma-ma;
nat-'ral born bee-hive,

You 'bout to starve me half to death. Now
Filled_ with hon-ey to the top. But

you could spare a kiss or two and still have plen-ty left. Oh, no, no,
I ain't greed-y, ba-by, all I want is all you got.

Copyright © 1959 by Elvis Presley Music Inc., New York, USA.
Carlin Music Corp., 14 New Burlington Street, London, W1X 1AE for the British Isles, British Empire
(excluding Canada, Australia and New Zealand) and the Republic of Ireland and Greece.

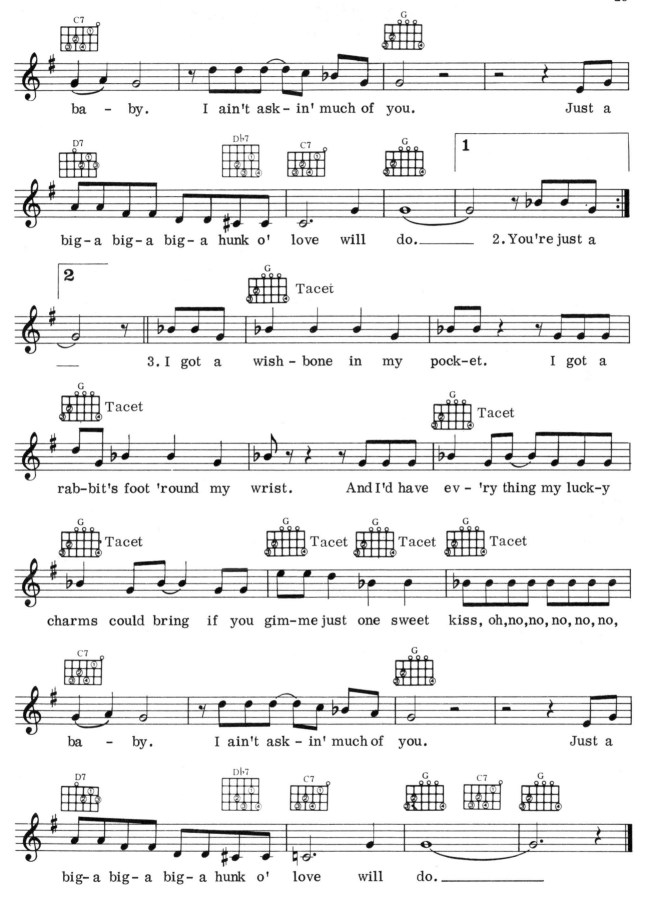

ONE NIGHT

WORDS & MUSIC BY
DAVE BARTHOLOMEW & PEARL KING

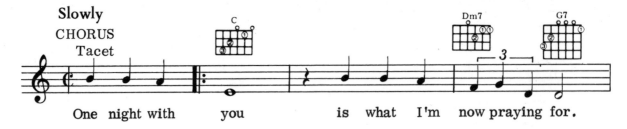

One night with you is what I'm now praying for.

The things that we two could plan would make my dreams come

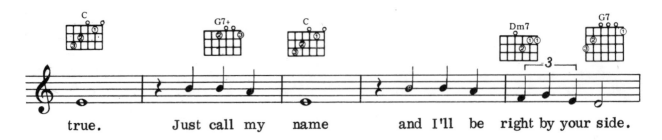

true. Just call my name and I'll be right by your side.

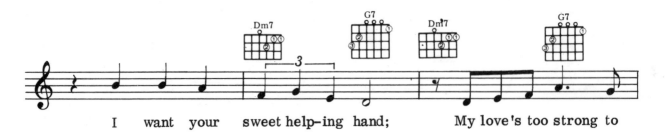

I want your sweet help-ing hand; My love's too strong to

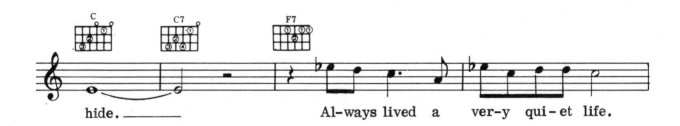

hide. _____ Al-ways lived a ver-y qui-et life.

Copyright © 1957 by Travis Music Inc.
All Rights for the United States and Canada assigned to Elvis Presley Music Inc.
Carlin Music Corp., 14 New Burlington Street, London, W1X 1AE for the British Isles and the British Empire
(excluding Canada, South Africa, Australia and New Zealand) and the Republic of Ireland.

I ain't nev – er did no wrong. Now I know that

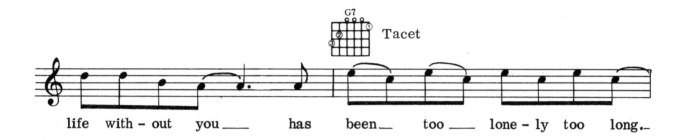

life with – out you ___ has been ___ too ___ lone – ly too long. ___

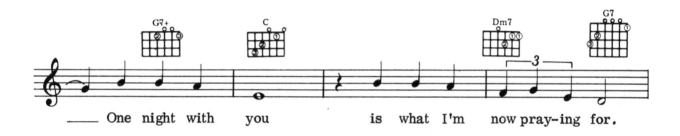

___ One night with you is what I'm now pray-ing for.

The things that we two could plan would make my dreams come

true. One night with true. ___

I NEED YOUR LOVE TONIGHT

Medium bright Rock

WORDS & MUSIC BY
SID WAYNE & BIX REICHNER

Oh, oh, I love you so.___ Uh, uh, can't

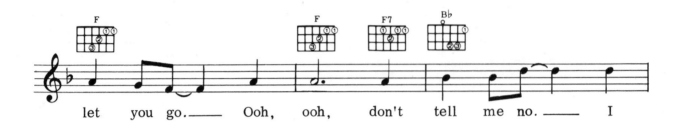

let you go.___ Ooh, ooh, don't tell me no.___ I

need your love to - night.___ Oh, gee, the way you kiss,___ Swee-

- dee, too good to miss.___Wow - whee, want more of this.___ I

need your love to - night. ___ I've been wait - in' just

Copyright © 1959 by Gladys Music Inc., New York, USA.
Carlin Music Corp., 14 New Burlington Street, London, W1X 1AE for the territory of the United Kingdom of Great Britain
and Northern Ireland, Eire, Israel, and the British Dominions, Colonies, Overseas Territories and Dependencies.
The use of this song with any other music is expressly prohibited.

STUCK ON YOU

Moderately
CHORUS

WORDS & MUSIC BY
AARON SCHROEDER & J. LESLIE MCFARLAND

You can shake an ap-ple off an ap-ple tree.___
Gon-na run my fin-gers thru your long black hair.___

shake - a shake - a, sug - ar, but you'll nev - er shake me.___ Uh-uh - uh.___
Squeeze you ___ tight - er than a griz - zly bear.___ Uh-huh - huh.___

___ No - sir - ee.___ uh - uh.
___ Yes-sir - ee.___ uh - huh.

I'm gon - na stick like glue.___ Stick be-cause I'm

Tacet
1 **2**
Stuck on you. you. Hide in the kitch-en,

hide in the hall. Ain't gon - na do you no

Copyright © 1960 by Gladys Music Inc., New York, 19, NY.
Carlin Music Corp., 14 New Burlington Street, London, W1X 1AE for the territory of Great Britain, Ireland, Eire,
Israel, and the British Dominions, Colonies, Overseas Territories and Dependencies
(excluding Canada, Australia and New Zealand).
The use of these lyrics with any other music is expressly prohibited.

WOODEN HEART

WORDS & MUSIC BY
FRED WISE, BEN WEISMAN, KAY TWOMEY &
BERTHOLD KAEMPFERT

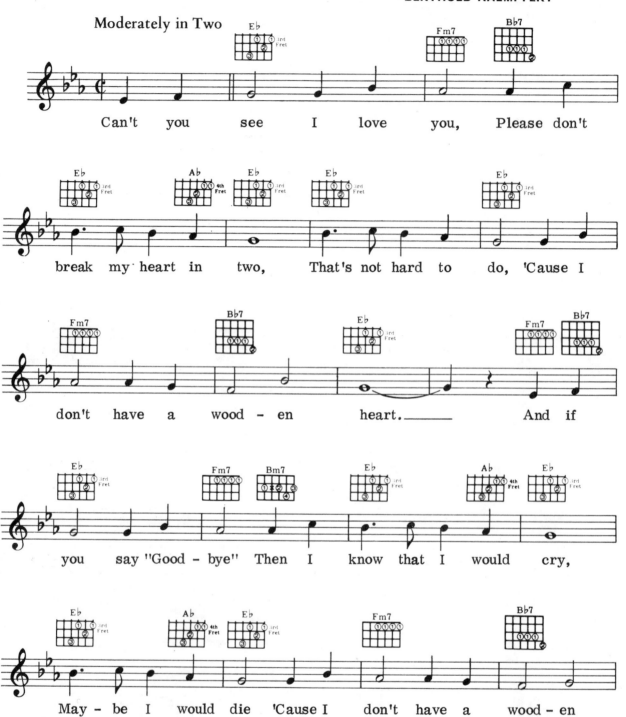

Copyright © 1960 by Gladys Music Inc., New York, USA.
Carlin Music Corp., 14 New Burlington Street, London, W1 for United Kingdom of Great Britain and Northern Ireland,
Eire, Israel, and the British Dominions, Colonies, Overseas Territories and Dependencies
(excluding Canada, Australia and New Zealand).
The use of this song with any other music is expressly prohibited.

heart._____ There's no strings up - on this

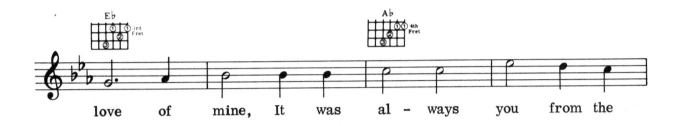

love of mine, It was al - ways you from the

start,_____ Treat me nice, treat me good, treat me

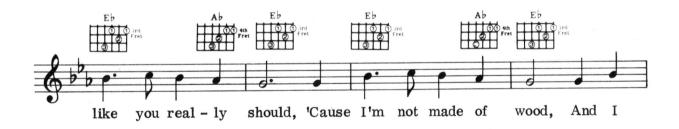

like you real - ly should, 'Cause I'm not made of wood, And I

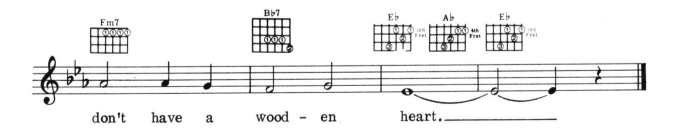

don't have a wood - en heart._____

[MARIE'S THE NAME]
HIS LATEST FLAME

WORDS & MUSIC BY
DOC POMUS & MORT SHUMAN

Moderately bright

A ver-y old friend came by to-day,
talked, and I heard him say

'Cause he was tell-in' ev-'ry-one in town
That she had the long-est black-est hair,

'bout the love that he just found. And Marie's the name
pret-ti-est green eyes an-y-where.

of his lat-est flame. He talked and

Though I smiled, the tears in-side were a-burnin'

I wished him luck and then he said good-bye.

Copyright © 1961 by Elvis Presley Music Inc., New York, USA.
Carlin Music Corp., 14 New Burlington Street, London, W1X 1AE for the British Empire
(excluding Canada, Australia and New Zealand) and the Republic of Ireland, Greece and Israel.

Can't Help Falling In Love

WORDS & MUSIC BY
GEORGE WEISS, HUGO PERETTI &
LUIGI CREATORE

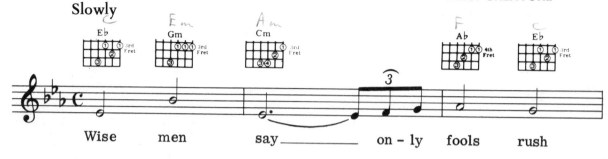

Slowly

Wise men say _____ on - ly fools rush

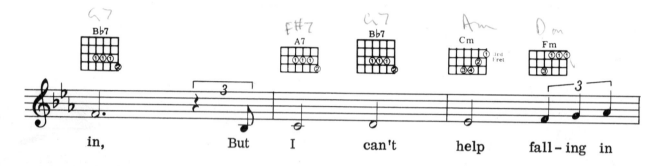

in, But I can't help fall - ing in

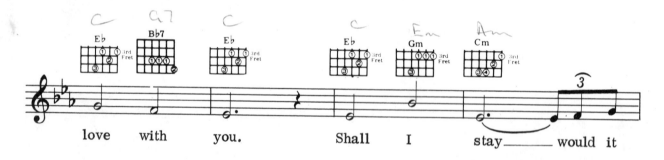

love with you. Shall I stay _____ would it

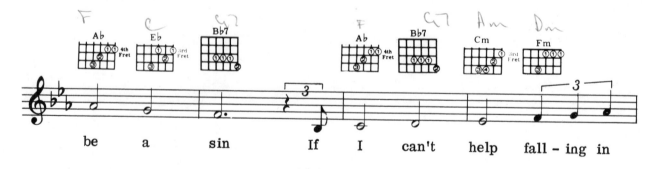

be a sin If I can't help fall - ing in

Copyright © 1961 by Gladys Music Inc., New York, USA.
Carlin Music Corp., 14 New Burlington Street, London, W1X 1AE for the British Isles, British Empire
(excluding Canada, Australia, and New Zealand) and the Republic of Ireland, Greece and Israel.

41

GOOD LUCK CHARM

WORDS & MUSIC BY
AARON SCHROEDER & WALLY GOLD

Moderately

1. Don't want a four leaf clov-er;
2. Don't want a sil-ver dol-lar,
3. I found a luck-y pen-ny, I'd

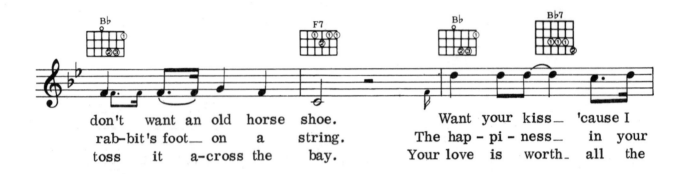

don't want an old horse shoe. Want your kiss_ 'cause I
rab-bit's foot_ on a string. The hap-pi-ness_ in your
toss it a-cross the bay. Your love is worth_ all the

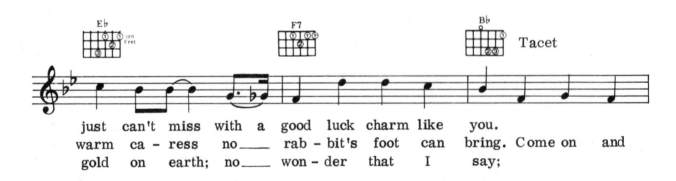

just can't miss with a good luck charm like you.
warm ca-ress no_ rab-bit's foot can bring. Come on and
gold on earth; no_ won-der that I say;

be my lit-tle good luck charm. Uh-huh-huh,_ you sweet de-

©Copyright 1961 by Gladys Music Incorporated, New York 19, New York, U.S.A.
International Copyright Secured. Made in England. All Rights Reserved.
Carlin Music Corporation, 14 New Burlington Street, London W I, for the British Isles,
British Empire (excluding Canada, Australia, New Zealand, South Africa) and the Republic of Ireland, Greece & Israel.

light.   I want a   good luck charm a-hang-in'   on   my arm   To have,

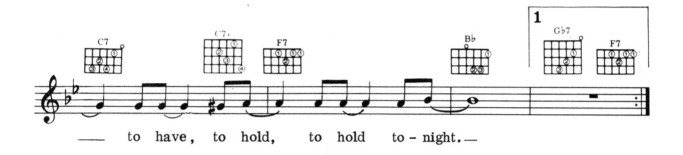

1

—— to have,   to   hold,   to hold   to - night. ——

2   Tacet

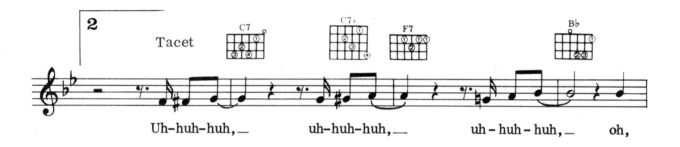

Uh–huh–huh, ——   uh–huh–huh, ——   uh – huh – huh, ——   oh,

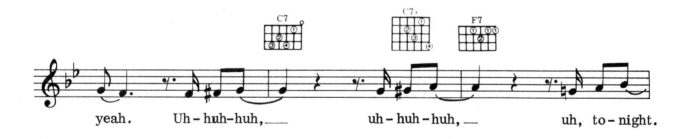

yeah.   Uh – huh–huh, ——   uh – huh – huh, ——   uh, to - night.

1   *Return to Chorus, take 2nd Ending*   **2**

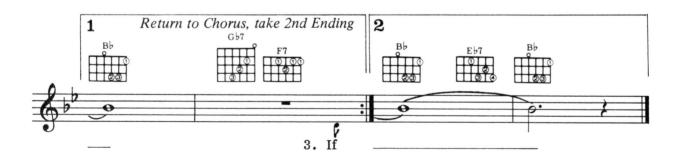

——   3. If   ————————————

SHE'S NOT YOU

WORDS & MUSIC BY
JERRY LEIBER, MIKE STOLLER &
DOC POMUS

© Copyright 1962 by Elvis Presley Music Inc., New York, USA.
Carlin Music Corp., 14 New Burlington Street, London, W1X 1AE for the territory of United Kingdom of Great Britain and
Northern Ireland, Eire, and the British Dominion Colonies, Overseas Territories and Dependencies
(excluding Canada, Australia and New Zealand).

Return To Sender

Moderately
CHORUS

WORDS & MUSIC BY
OTIS BLACKWELL & WINFIELD SCOTT

I gave a let-ter to the post-man; ___
So then I dropped it in the mail-box ___

he put it in his sack. Bright and ear-ly next
and sent it Spe-cial D. Bright and ear-ly next

morn-ing ___ he brought my let-ter back. She wrote upon it:
morn-ing ___ it came right back to me.

Re-turn ___ to send-er, ad-dress un-

known No such number, no such

1

zone. We had ___ a quar-rel, a lov-er's

Copyright © 1962 by Elvis Presley Music Inc., New York, USA.
Carlin Music Corporation, 14 New Burlington Street, London, W1X 1AE for the United Kingdom of Great Britain
and Northern Ireland, South Africa, Eire, Israel, and the British Dominions, Colonies,
Overseas Territories and Dependencies (excluding Canada, Australia and New Zealand).

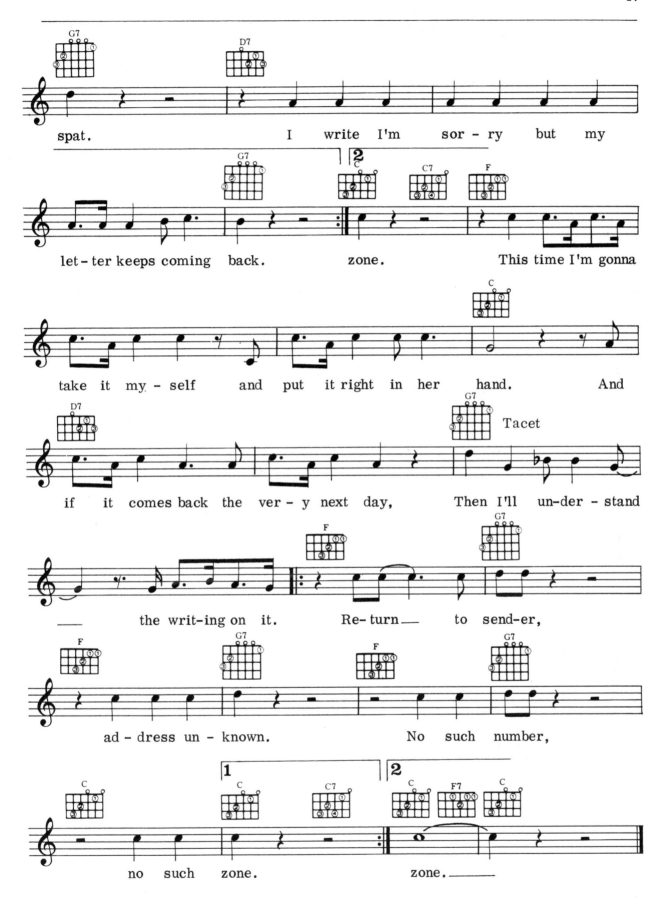

spat.   I   write   I'm   sor - ry   but   my

let - ter keeps coming back.   zone.   This time I'm gonna

take it my - self   and   put   it right   in   her   hand.   And

if   it comes back   the   ver - y next   day,   Then I'll un - der - stand

____   the writ-ing on   it.   Re - turn ___   to send-er,

ad - dress un - known.   No   such   number,

no   such   zone.   zone. ___

You're The Devil In Disguise

WORDS & MUSIC BY
BILL GIANT, BERNIE BAUM &
FLORENCE KAYE

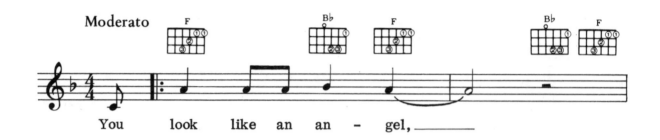

You look like an an - gel,_____

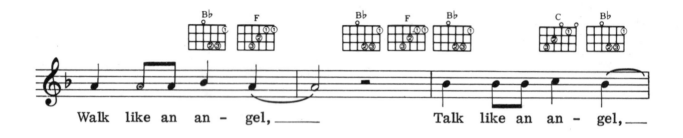

Walk like an an - gel,_____ Talk like an an - gel,___

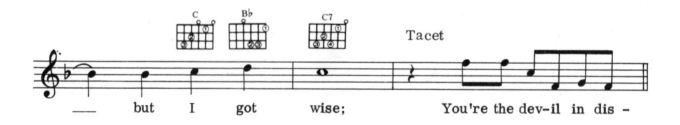

___ but I got wise; You're the dev-il in dis -

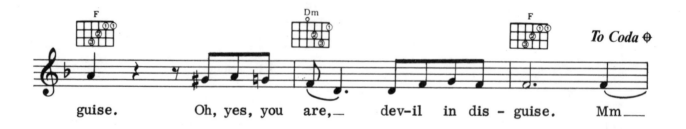

guise. Oh, yes, you are,___ dev-il in dis - guise. Mm___

©Copyright 1963 by Elvis Presley Music Incorporated, New York, N.Y., U.S.A.
International Copyright Secured. Made in England. All Rights Reserved.
Carlin Music Corporation, 14 New Burlington Street, London W1, for the British Isles and the British Empire
(excluding Canada, South Africa, Australia and New Zealand) and the Republic or Ireland.

1. You fooled me — with your kiss – es,
2. I thought that — I was in heav – en,

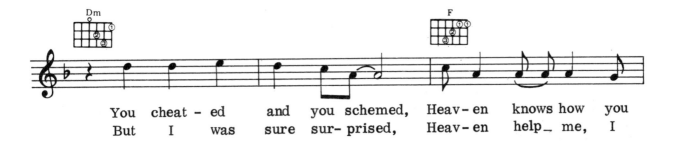

You cheat – ed and you schemed, Heav-en knows how you
But I was sure sur- prised, Heav-en help — me, I

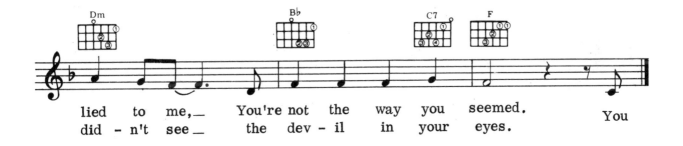

lied to me, — You're not the way you seemed. You
did – n't see — the dev – il in your eyes.

✛ CODA *Repeat ad lib. fading-out*

— Dev-il in dis – guise, Oh, yes, you are. Dev-il in dis -

THERE GOES MY EVERYTHING

WORDS & MUSIC BY
DALLAS FRAZIER

Moderately Slow

VERSE

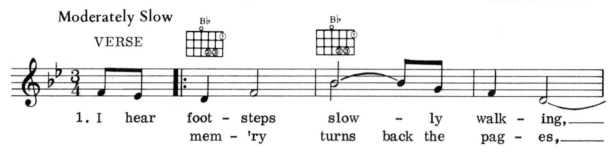

1. I hear foot-steps slow-ly walk-ing,____
mem-'ry turns back the pag-es,____

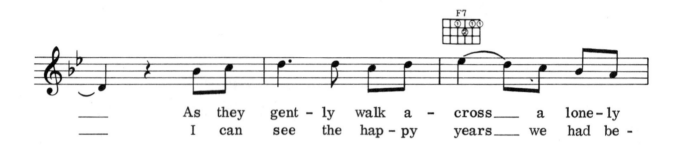

____ As they gent-ly walk a-cross____ a lone-ly
____ I can see the hap-py years____ we had be-

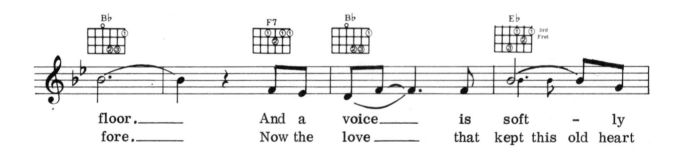

floor.____ And a voice____ is soft-ly
fore.____ Now the love____ that kept this old heart

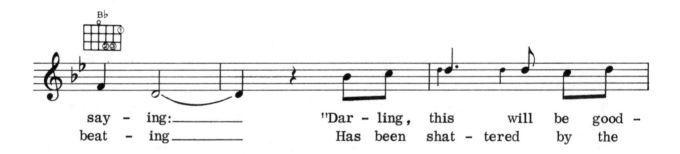

say-ing:____ "Dar-ling, this will be good-
beat-ing____ Has been shat-tered by the

© Copyright 1965, 1966 by Blue Crest Music Inc., and Husky Music Inc.
All rights for the world (excluding USA. and Canada) controlled by Burlington Music Co. Ltd.,
9 Albert Embankment, London, S.E.1.

bye___ for-ev-er - more."___ There goes my
clos - ing of the door.___

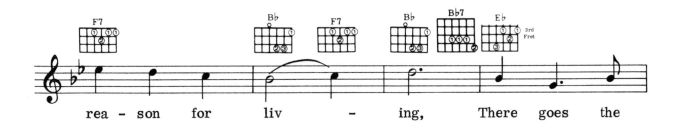

rea - son for liv - ing, There goes the

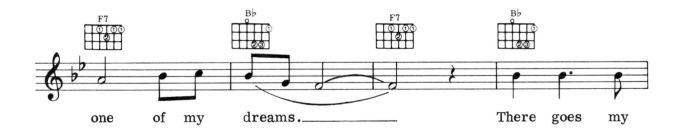

one of my dreams.___ There goes my

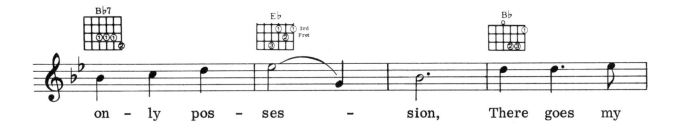

on - ly pos - ses - sion, There goes my

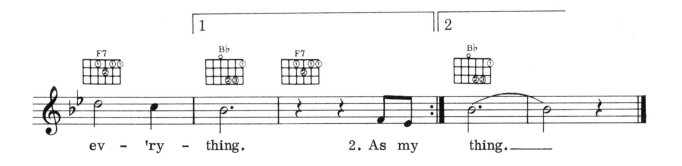

ev - 'ry - thing. 2. As my thing.___

Wild In The Country

WORDS & MUSIC BY
GEORGE WEISS, HUGO PERETTI &
LUIGI CREATORE

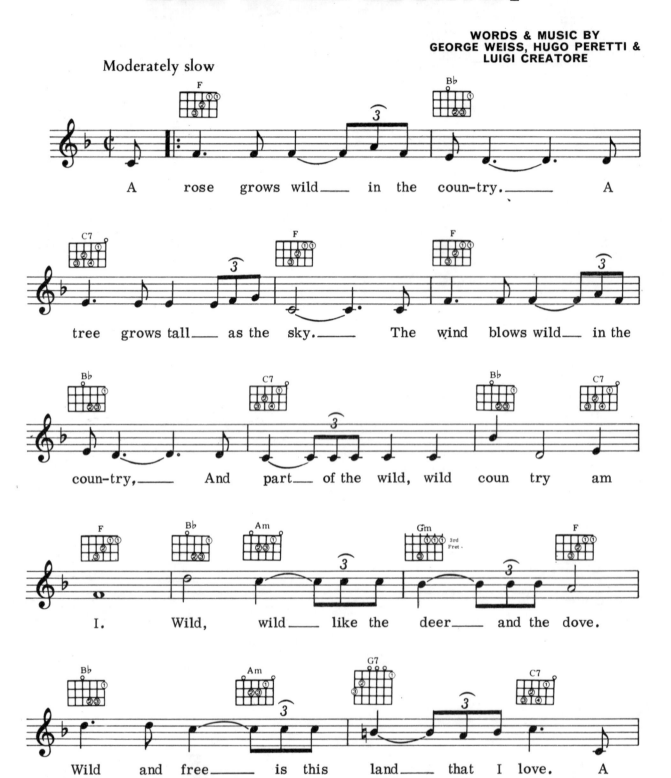

Moderately slow

A rose grows wild___ in the coun-try.___ A tree grows tall___ as the sky.___ The wind blows wild___ in the coun-try,___ And part___ of the wild, wild coun try am I. Wild, wild___ like the deer___ and the dove. Wild and free___ is this land___ that I love. A

Copyright © 1961 by Gladys Music Inc., New York, USA.
Carlin Music Corp., 14 New Burlington Street, London, W1X 1AE for the British Isles, British Empire
(excluding Canada, Australia and New Zealand) and the Republic of Ireland and Greece.

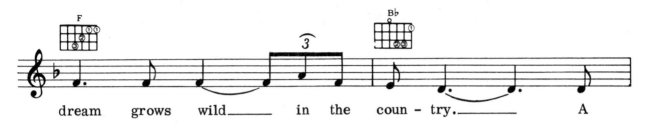

dream grows wild____ in the coun-try.____ A

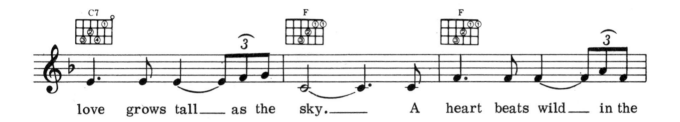

love grows tall___ as the sky.____ A heart beats wild___ in the

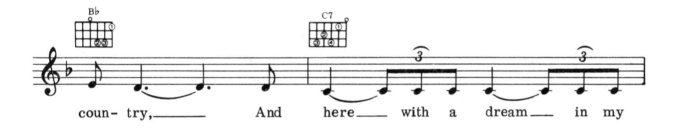

coun-try,____ And here___ with a dream___ in my

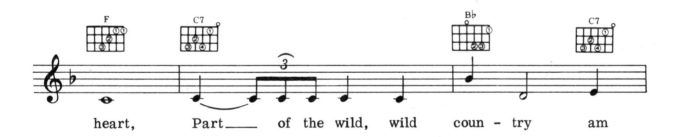

heart, Part___ of the wild, wild coun-try am

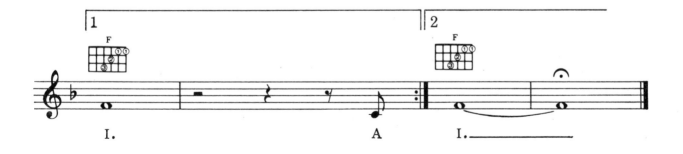

I.   A I.____

Rock-a-Hula Baby

WORDS & MUSIC BY
FRED WISE, BEN WEISMAN, DOLORES FULLER

Moderately bright

1. The way she moves her hips___ up to her
love to kiss___ my lit - tle
she could teach___ the palms a -

fin - ger tips,___ I feel I'm heav - en bound. And when she
hu - la miss,___ I nev - er get the chance. I wan - na
long the beach___ To sway when breez - es blow. And birds up

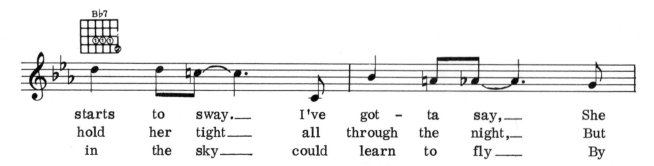

starts to sway.___ I've got - ta say,___ She
hold her tight___ all through the night,___ But
in the sky___ could learn to fly ___ By

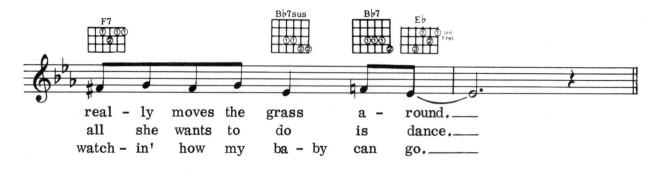

real - ly moves the grass a - round.___
all she wants to do is dance.___
watch - in' how my ba - by can go. _____

©Copyright 1961 by Gladys Music Incorporated, New York 19, N.Y.
International Copyright Secured. All Rights Reserved.
Carlin Music Corporation, 14 New Burlington Street, London W1, for the British Isles, British Empire
(excluding Canada, Australia and New Zealand) and the Republic of Ireland, Greece & Israel.

CHORUS

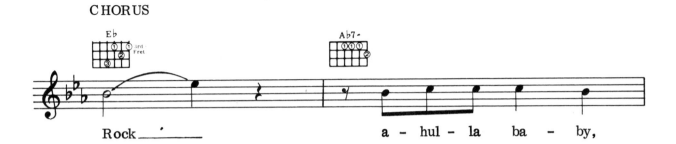

Rock_____ a - hul - la ba - by,

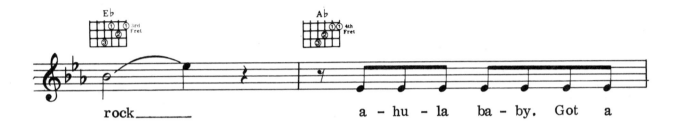

rock_____ a - hu - la ba - by. Got a

hu - la lu - lu from Hon - o - lu - lu, that

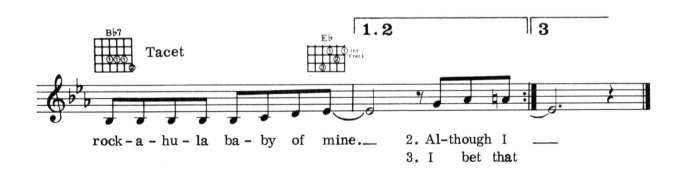

Tacet

1.2   3

rock-a-hu-la ba-by of mine.___ 2. Al-though I ___
3. I   bet that

SURRENDER

ORIGINAL ITALIAN LYRICS BY
G. B. DE CURTIS
MUSIC BY
E. DE CURTIS

ENGLISH WORDS & ADAPTATION BY
DOC POMUS
MORT SHULMAN

Moderately bright

When we kiss my heart's on fire re_____ Burning

with a strange de - si - re._____ And I know each time I

kiss you_____ That your heart's on fi - re too.

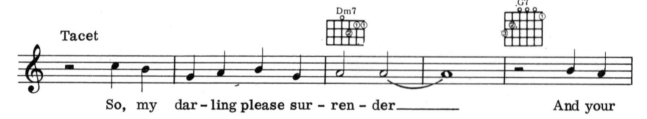

Tacet

So, my dar - ling please sur - ren - der_____ And your

love so warm and ten - der._____ Let me hold you im my

arms, dear,_____ While the moon shines bright a - bove._____

©Copyright 1960 by Elvis Presley Music Incorporated, New York, N.Y.
International Copyright Secured. All Rights Reserved.
Carlin Music Corporation, 14 New Burlington Street, London W1 for the British Isles and the British Empire
(excluding Canada, South Africa, Australia and New Zealand) and the Republic of Ireland.

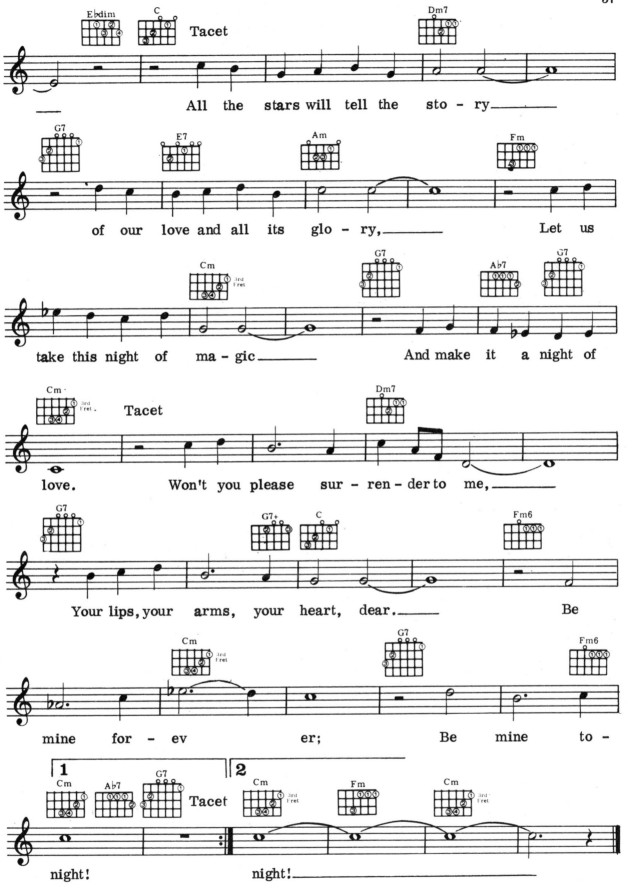

All the stars will tell the sto - ry_____

of our love and all its glo - ry,_____ Let us

take this night of ma - gic_____ And make it a night of

love. Won't you please sur - ren - der to me,_____

Your lips, your arms, your heart, dear._____ Be

mine for - ev er; Be mine to -

night! night!_____

THERE'S ALWAYS ME

WORDS & MUSIC BY
DON ROBERTSON

Moderately slow

When the evening shad-ows fall, And you're wond'ring who to call, For a lit-tle com-pa-ny There's al-ways me. Or if your great ro-mance should end, And you're lonesome for a friend, Dar-ling, you need nev-er be; There's al-ways me. I don't seem to mind some how Play-ing sec-ond fid-dle now Some-day you'll

©Copyright 1961 by Gladys Music Incorporated, New York 19, New York, U.S.A.
International Copyright Secured. All Rights Reserved.
Carlin Music Corporation, 14 New Burlington Street, London W1, for the British Isles, British Empire
(excluding Canada, Australia and New Zealand) and the Republic of Ireland, Greece & Israel.

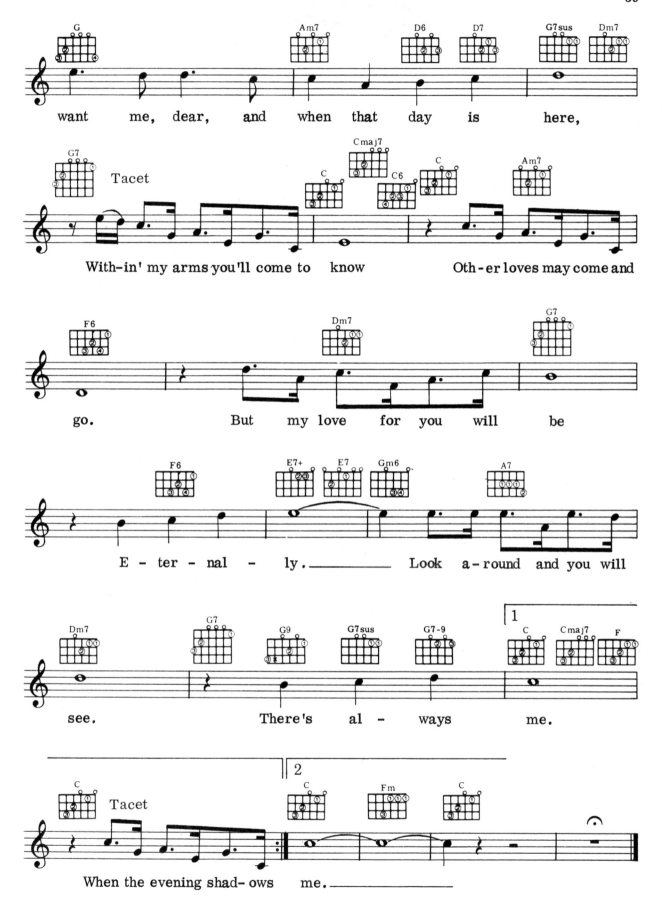

MY BOY

MUSIC BY
CLAUDE FRANCOIS & JEAN-PIERRE
BOURTAYRE

WORDS BY
BILL MARTIN & PHIL COULTER

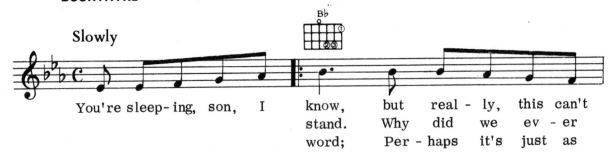

Slowly

You're sleep-ing, son, I know, but real - ly, this can't
stand. Why did we ev - er
word; Per - haps it's just as

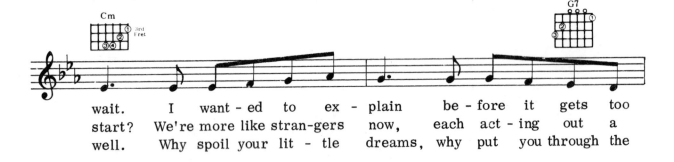

wait. I want - ed to ex - plain be - fore it gets too
start? We're more like stran-gers now, each act - ing out a
well. Why spoil your lit - tle dreams, why put you through the

late. _____ For your moth - er and
part. _____ I have laughed, I have
hell. _____ Life is no fair - y

me, Love has fi - nal - ly died; This is no hap - py
cried; I have lost ev - 'ry game, tak-en all I can
tale, as one day you will know, but now you're just a

© Copyright 1971 Espiegle Music, Isabelle Musique, Paris, for the world.
© Copyright 1971 Mews Music Limited, London, for the British Isles,
the British Commonwealth (except Canada), USA and Eire.

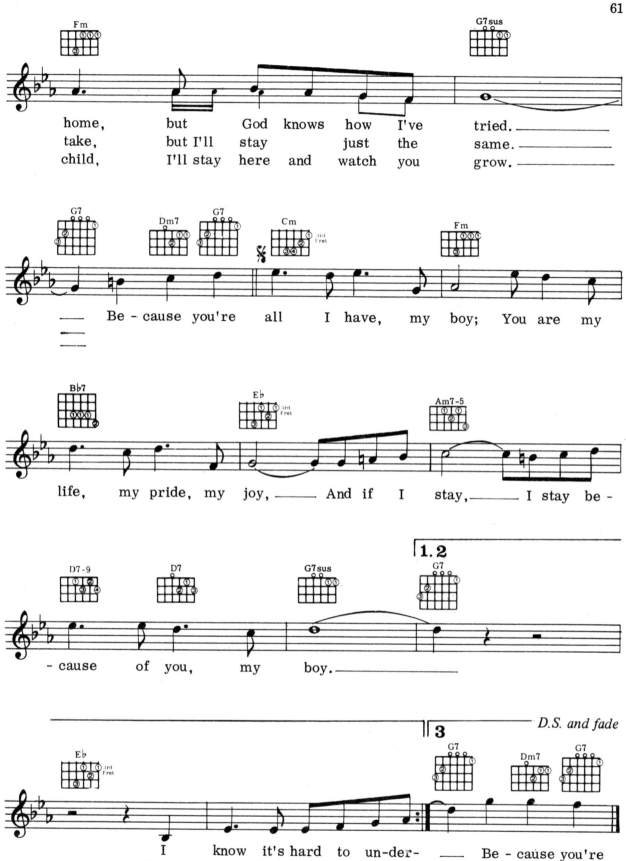

Heartbreak Hotel

WORDS & MUSIC BY
MAE BOREN AXTON, TOMMY DURDEN
& ELVIS PRESLEY

Blues tempo

Now since my ba - by left me I've found a new place to dwell.

Down at the end of lone-ly street at Heart - break Ho - tel, I'm so

lone - ly, I'm so lone - ly, I'm so lone - ly that I could

die! And tho' it's al - ways crowd - ed you can

still find some room for bro - ken heart - ed lov - ers to

cry there in the gloom and be so lone - ly, oh, so

Copyright © 1956 by Tree Publishing Co. Inc., 146 W. 54th St., New York.
For all countries of the world (excluding USA and Canada).
Belwin Mills Music Ltd., 250 Purley Way, Croydon.

lone - ly,____ oh, so lone - ly_____ they could die! The

bell-hop's tears keep flow - ing, the __ desk clerk's dressed in black ,
if your ba - by leaves and you have a tale to ____ tell,

they've been so long_____ on lone - ly street they
just take a walk____ down lone - ly street to

nev - er will_____ go back and they're so
Heart - break_____ Ho - tel where you'll be

lone - ly_____ oh they're so lone - ly,_____ They're so
lone - ly_____ and I'll be lone - ly, ____we'll be so

1.

2.

lone - ly_____ they pray to die. So die.
lone - ly _____ that we could

I Love You Because

WORDS & MUSIC BY
LEON PAYNE

CHORUS

1. I love you be - cause you un - der - stand, dear,____
love you be - cause my heart is lighter er ____

____ ev - 'ry sin - gle thing I try to do.____
____ ev - 'ry time I'm walk - ing by your side.____

____ You're al - ways there to lend a help - ing hand, dear,____
____ I love you be - cause the fu - ture's bright - er.____

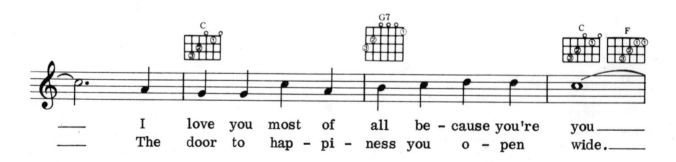

____ I love you most of all be - cause you're you____
____ The door to hap - pi - ness you o - pen wide.____

© Copyright 1949 by Acuff-Rose Publications, Tennessee, USA.
Bourne Music Ltd., 34-36 Maddox Street, London, W1R 9PD for the British Empire and Commonwealth of Nations
(excluding Canada, Australia and New Zealand) and Eire.

Lawdy Miss Clawdy

**WORDS & MUSIC BY
LLOYD PRICE**

Slow Rock

1. Oh! now Law - dy, Law - dy, Law - dy, Miss
-cause I give you all_____ my

Claw - dy, Girl! You sure look good to me_____
mon - ey, Girl! You just won't treat me right_____

_____ Well_____ please don't ex - cite me ba - by
_____ You like to ball_____ in the morn - ing

Tho'_____ it can't_____ be me_____
don't_____ come back un - til night_____

2. Be

Copyright © 1952 by Venice Music Inc.
All rights reserved including the right of public performance for profit.
Carlin Music Corp., 14 New Burlington Street, London, W1X 1AE.
for the British Empire (excluding Canada, Australasia, New Zealand and South Africa) and the Republic of Ireland.

67

3. I'm gon-na   tell,   tell my ma - ma, Lawd, I'm
4. Well now   Law-dy, Law-dy, Law-dy   Miss
5. Well so   bye,   bye,   bye,   bye,

gon - na   tell her what   you   been   do - ing to   me
Claw - dy   Girl!   you   sure   look   good to to   me
ba - by   Girl!   I   won't   be   trou - ble no - more

I'm gon - na   tell ev-'ry-bo - dy that   I'm
You   just wheel-ing and rock-ing ba - by
Good - bye   Claw-dy   oh dar - ling

down   in mis - er - y
you're just   as fine as   you can be
down   the road   I'll   go

4. Well   now
5. Well   so

LONG TALL SALLY

WORDS & MUSIC BY
ENOTRIS JOHNSON, RICHARD PENNIMAN
& ROBERT BLACKWELL

Bright Rock tempo

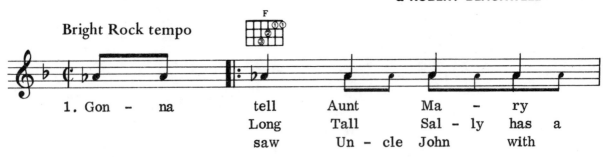

1. Gon - na tell Aunt Ma - ry
Long Tall Sal - ly has a
saw Un - cle John with

'bout Un - cle John, He says he has the blues, But he
lot on the ball, And no - bod - y cares if she's
Long Tall ___ Sal - ly, He saw Aunt Ma - ry com - in' And he

has a lot of fun,
long ___ and ___ tall, Oh, ba - by yes ___
ducked back in the al - ley,

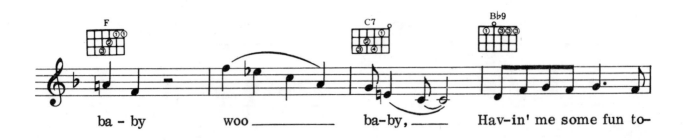

ba - by woo ___ ba - by, ___ Hav - in' me some fun to-

© Copyright 1956 by Venice Music Inc., Hollywood, U.S.A.
Southern Music Publishing Company Limited, 8 Denmark Street, London, W.C.2.
for the British Commonwealth (excluding Canada and Australasia).

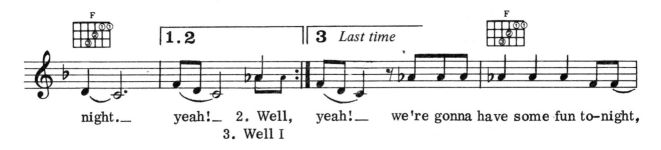

night.__ yeah!_ 2. Well, yeah!__ we're gonna have some fun to-night,
3. Well I

__ Gon-na have some fun to-night__ woo!_ We're gon-na

have some fun to-night,__ Ev-'ry-thing will be all right.

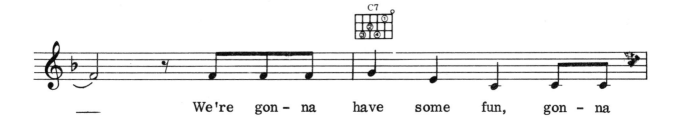

__ We're gon-na have some fun, gon-na

have some fun to-night!_____

Mean Woman Blues

WORDS & MUSIC BY
CLAUDE DE METRUIS

Medium Rock

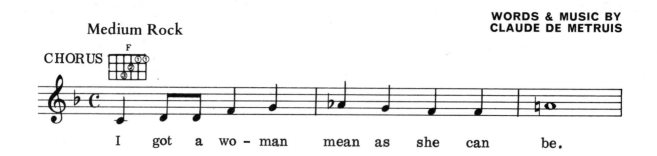

CHORUS

I got a wo-man mean as she can be.

I got a wo-man mean as she can be.

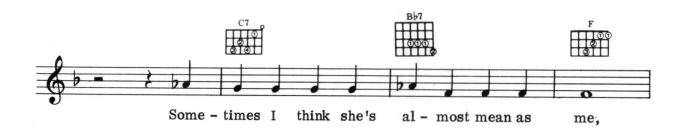

Some-times I think she's al-most mean as me;

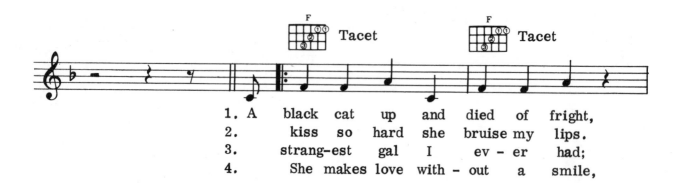

Tacet   Tacet

1. A black cat up and died of fright,
2. kiss so hard she bruise my lips.
3. strang-est gal I ev-er had;
4. She makes love with-out a smile,

Copyright © 1957 by Gladys Music Inc., New York.
Carlin Music Corp., 14 New Burlington Street, London, W1X 1AE
for the British Isles and the British Empire (excluding Canada, South Africa, Australia and New Zealand)
and the Republic of Ireland.

'Cause she crossed his path last night.
Hurts so good my heart just flips.
Nev-er hap-py 'less she's mad.
Ooh hot dog, that drives me wild.

Oh, I got a wo-man

mean as she can be. Some-times I think she's

1.2.3

al-most mean as me. 2. She
3. The
4. ____

4

me. Some-times I think she's

al-most mean as me.

PARALYZED

Bright shuffle

WORDS & MUSIC BY
OTIS BLACKWELL & ELVIS PRESLEY

Copyright © 1956 by Shalimar Music Inc., New York, USA.
Rights assigned 1956 to Elvis Presley Music Inc., New York, USA.
Carlin Music Corp., 14 New Burlington Street, London, W1X 1AE for the territory of the United Kingdom of Great Britain
and Northern Ireland, Eire, Israel, and the British Dominions, Colonies, Overseas Territories and Dependencies
The use of this song with any other music is expressly prohibited

WHEN MY BLUE MOON TURNS TO GOLD AGAIN

WORDS & MUSIC BY
WILEY WALKER & GENE SULLIVAN

Moderato
VERSE

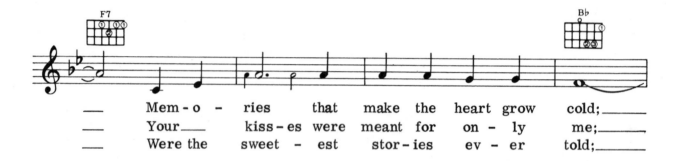

1. Mem- o - ries that lin - ger in my heart,____
   lips that used to thrill me so,____
   cas -tles we built of dreams to - geth - er ____

____ Mem- o - ries that make the heart grow cold;____
____ Your____ kiss- es were meant for on - ly me;____
____ Were the sweet - est stor - ies ev - er told;____

____ But some day they'll live a - gain, sweet - heart,____
____ In my dreams they live a - gain, sweet - heart,____
____ May - be we will live them all a - gain,____

And my blue moon a - gain will turn to
But my gold - en moon is just a mem - o -
And my blue moon a - gain will turn to

© Copyright 1941 by Peer International Corporation, 1619 Broadway, New York, 19, USA.
Southern Music Publishing Co. Ltd., 8 Denmark Street, London, WC2H 8LT.

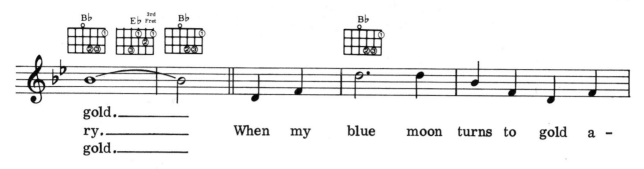

gold._____
ry._____ When my blue moon turns to gold a -
gold._____

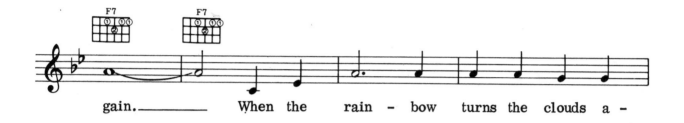

gain._____ When the rain - bow turns the clouds a -

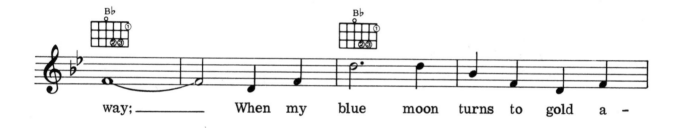

way;_____ When my blue moon turns to gold a -

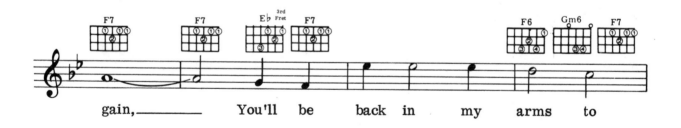

gain,_____ You'll be back in my arms to

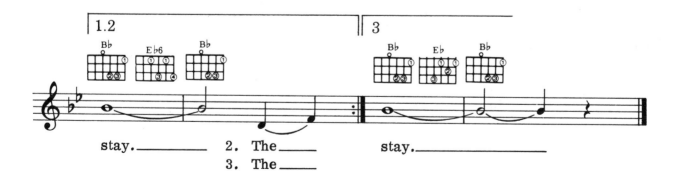

stay._____ 2. The____   stay._____
3. The____

I GOT STUNG

Bright Rock tempo

WORDS & MUSIC BY
AARON SCHROEDER & DAVID HILL

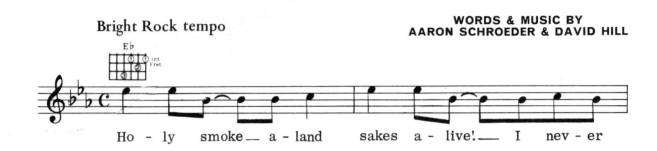

Ho - ly smoke __ a - land sakes a - live! __ I nev - er

thought this could hap-pen to me. _____ Mm, _____

Yeah! Mm, _____ Yeah! I got stung by a sweet hon-ey
she had all that I want-ed and

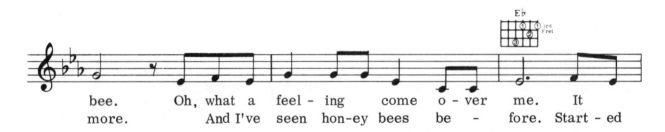

bee. Oh, what a feel - ing come o - ver me. It
more. And I've seen hon-ey bees be - fore. Start - ed

start - ed in my eyes, crept up to my __ head, F -
buzz - in' in my ear, buzz - in' in my brain, Got

Copyright © 1958 by Gladys Music Inc., New York, USA.
Carlin Music Corp., 14 New Burlington Street, London, W1X 1AE for the British Isles, British Empire
(excluding Canada, South Africa, Australia and New Zealand) and the Republic of Ireland.

77

-lew to my heart— till I was stung dead
stung— all o-ver but I feel no pain. I'm done, Uh -

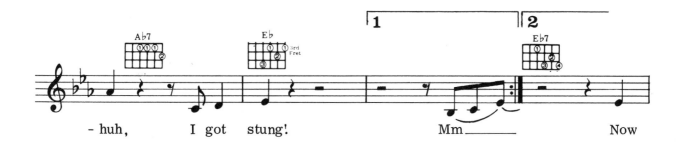

- huh, I got stung! Mm————— Now

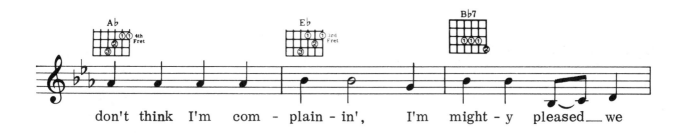

don't think I'm com-plain-in', I'm might-y pleased— we

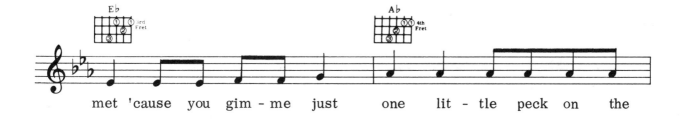

met 'cause you gim-me just one lit-tle peck on the

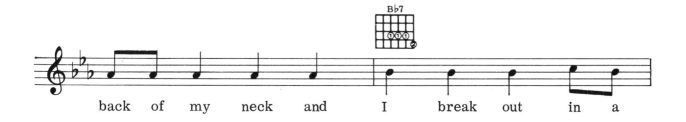

back of my neck and I break out in a

cold cold sweat. If I live to a hun‑dred and

two, I won't let no‑bod‑y sting me but

you. I'll be buzz‑in' round your hive ev‑'ry

day at five, and I'm nev‑er gon‑na leave___ once

I ar‑rive 'cause I'm done, uh‑huh, I got

1 stung!

2 Mm,_____ stung._____

IN THE GHETTO

**WORDS & MUSIC BY
SCOTT DAVIS**

Copyright © 1969 by B-n-B Music Inc., and Elvis Presley Music Inc., New York, USA.
Carlin Music Corp., 14 New Burlington Street, London, W1X 1AE for the territory of the United Kingdom of Great
Britain and Northern Ireland, Eire and the British Dominions, Colonies, Overseas Territories and Dependencies
(excluding Canada, Australia and New Zealand).
The use of this song with any other music is expressly prohibited.

do we sim - ply turn our heads and look the oth - er way? Well, the

world turns _____ and a hun-gry lit-tle boy with the run-ny nose

plays in the street as the cold ___ wind blows, ___ in the

Ghet - to. _____ And his hun-ger burns, _____

And he starts to roam ___ the streets ___ at night, and he

learns how to steal and he learns ___ how to fight, in the

Ghet - to. _____ And then one night, in des-per-a - tion, a

young man — breaks a-way, ——— He buys a gun, — steals a car, —

tries to run, — but he won't get far, and his ma-ma cries. ———

As the crowd gath-ers 'round an an - gry young man, face

down — in the street with a gun — in his hand, — in the

Ghet - to. ——— And as her young man dies,

On a cold and grey Chi - ca - go morn - in', an-

-oth-er lit-tle ba-by child — is born, in the Ghet-to. ———

DON'T CRY DADDY

Moderate with feeling

WORDS & MUSIC BY
SCOTT DAVIS

1. To - day I stum - bled from __ my bed, __ with
2. Why are chil - dren al - ways first __ to

thun - der crash - ing in _____ my head, My
feel the pain and hurt _____ the worst, it's

pil - low still __ wet from last night's tears.
true, but some - how it just don't seem right.

And as I think of giv - ing up, a voice __
'Cause ev - 'ry time I cry __ I know it hurts __

__ in - side my cof - fee cup, kept
__ my lit - tle chil - dren so, I

Copyright © 1969 by B-n-B Music Inc. and Elvis Presley Music Inc., New York, USA.
Carlin Music Corp., 14 New Burlington Street, London, W1X 1AE for the territory of the United Kingdom of
Great Britain and Northern Ireland, Eire, Israel, and the British Dominions, Colonies, Overseas Territories and
Dependencies (excluding Canada, Australia and New Zealand).
The use of this song with any other music is expressly prohibited.

cry - ing but _____ will it be and ring - ing in my
won - der _____ will it be the same to

CHORUS

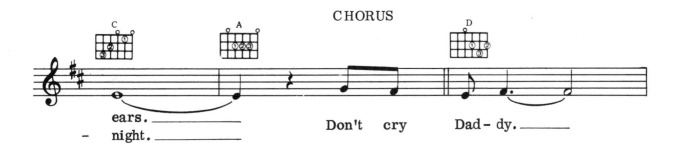

ears. _____ Don't cry Dad - dy. _____
- night. _____

Dad-dy, please don't cry; _____ Dad-dy,

you've still got me and lit - tle Tom - my, To -

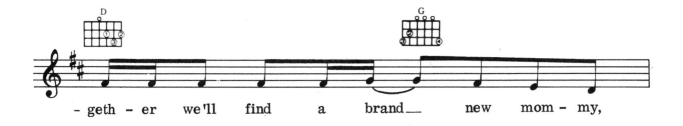

- geth - er we'll find a brand _____ new mom - my,

Dad - dy, Dad - dy, please laugh a - gain, ___

Dad - dy, ride ___ us on your back a - gain, ___ Oh,

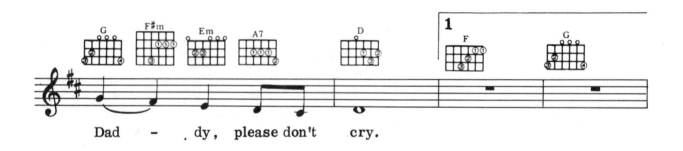

Dad - dy, please don't cry.

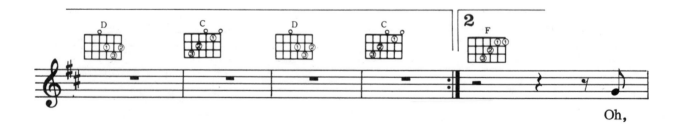

Oh,

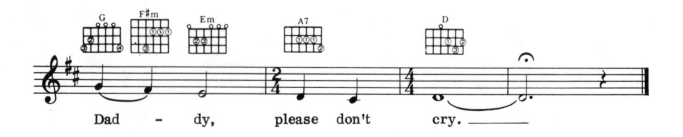

Dad - dy, please don't cry. ___

TUTTI FRUTTI

WORDS & MUSIC BY
R. PENNIMAN, D. LA BOSTRIE &
JOE LUBIN

Bright Rock 'n' Roll tempo

CHORUS

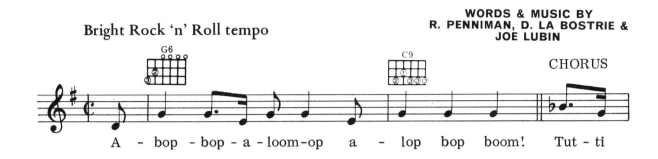

A - bop - bop - a - loom-op a - lop bop boom! Tut - ti

Frut - ti au rut - ti, Tut - ti Frut - ti au

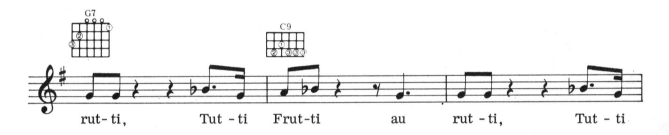

rut - ti, Tut - ti Frut-ti au rut - ti, Tut - ti

Frut - ti au rut - ti, Tut - ti Frut-ti au

rut - ti. A - bop - bop a - loom-op a - lop bop boom!

© Copyright 1955 by Venice Music Inc., Hollywood, U.S.A.
Assigned to Venice Music Ltd., 121 Ledbury Road, London W11.
for U.K., Eire, British Commonwealth (excluding Canada and
Australasia) and the Continent of Europe.

VERSE

she's the the gal I love the best.
pret - ty lit - lte Su - zy's the gal for me.
same kind of fla - vor when I'm kiss-ing you. Tut - ti
mean the same fla - vor of your sweet lips.
im - i - ta - tion fla - vor of you know what.

CHORUS

Frut- ti au rut-ti Tut - ti Frut-ti au

rut - ti Tut - ti Frut - ti au rut - ti Tut - ti

Frut-ti au rut-ti Tut-ti Frutti au rut - ti A

1   **2**

bop-bop a-loom-op a - lop bop boom!2.I got a
3. I got a
4. You're the
5. Won't you lop bop boom!

"UNTIL IT'S TIME FOR YOU TO GO"

**WORDS & MUSIC BY
BUFFY SAINTE-MARIE**

© Copyright 1965 & 1972 by Gypsy Boy Music Inc.
All rights for the territory of the United Kingdom and Eire controlled by
Essex Music International Ltd., Dumbarton House, 19-20 Poland Street, London, W.1.
International Copyright Secured. All rights including public performance for profit. Made in England.
Any adaptation of this work without the consent of the owner is an infringement of copyright.

never in my life see you a-gain,_____ still I'll

stay un-til it's time for you to go._____

Don't ask_ why of me, Don't ask_

how of me, Don't ask_ for-ev-er_ of

me. Love me,_ love me_ now._____ You're not a

D.S. al Coda

✛ *CODA*

stay un-til it's time for you to go._____